Contents

Answers to the questions are on the back of the Pull-out Poster in the centre of the book.

Published by Coordination Group Publications Ltd.

Contributors:
Taissa Csaky
Chris Dennett
Dominic Hall
Tim Major
Katherine Reed
Claire Thompson
James Paul Wallis

ISBN 1-84146-256-X

Groovy website: www.cgpbooks.co.uk
Jolly bits of clipart from CorelDRAW
Printed by Elanders Hindson, Newcastle upon Tyne.

With thanks to Christine Tinkler and Glenn Rogers for the proofreading.

Background

You have to eat food to stay alive.
Food gives you energy and helps you grow.

Q1   Look at the pictures below. Tick (✓) the boxes under food people eat.

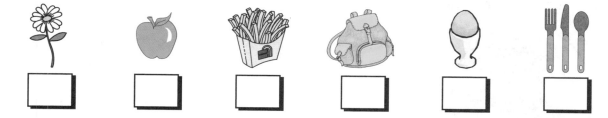

Q2 a) (Circle) the foods which you eat for school lunch.

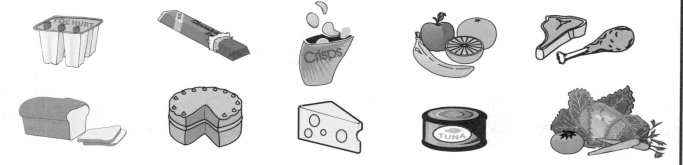

b)   Write the names of two other foods you eat.

1) ....   2) ....

Q3   Draw what you would most like to eat for school lunch on the plate below.

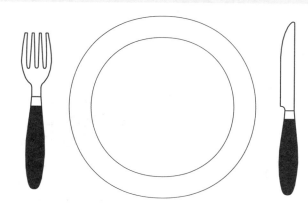

Food — for thought, but mostly for eating...

People eat food and it tastes good. That is all you need to know to start off with.
By the end of this book you will know more than your dentist about teeth and eating.

Naming Foods

All animals need to eat, including humans.
Here are just a few of the different things we gobble up...

Q1 Write the names of the foods in the boxes below the pictures.
I have done the first one for you.

Spaghetti

Food Groups

Similar foods can be grouped together.
For example pears and oranges go together because they are both fruit.

Q1   Draw all the foods from the last page in the correct food group boxes.   [Clue: two pictures go in each box.]

MEAT	FISH

FATTY FOOD	SUGARY FOOD

STARCHY FOOD	FRUIT AND VEGETABLES

Food groups — a piece of cake...

Some foods fit nicely into a group — easy. But some foods go in more than one group.
A toffee apple is a fruit and a sugary food... (And a food that pulled two of my teeth out!)

Foods for Growth

We need different food to do different things. Some foods help us to grow...

Q1 Why do you need food? Put a tick (✔) next to the correct answer below.

☐ To keep your parents happy.

☐ So you can grow, move and stay healthy.

☐ To give the farmers something to do.

☐ To keep your teeth clean.

Q2 Which plate has foods on it that are better for **helping us grow**?
Put a tick (✔) in the box next to the correct plate.

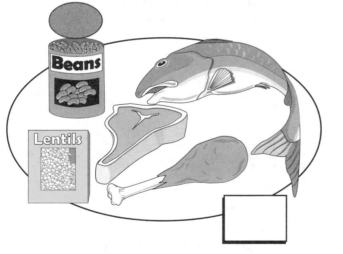

Q3 Look at the plate you have ticked. Write down the **names** of all the foods on it.

These five foods help you to grow: ....

....

....

Food for growth...

You need food to stay alive, but you have to eat the right things.
Some foods help you to grow — if you don't eat enough you won't grow properly.

Foods for Activity

All animals are active. Some need to chase their food, some need to run away and some need to kick a ball into the top corner of a goal.

Q1 Use words from the feet to finish these sentences about food.

[Clue: You won't need all the words.]

All .... including ....

need .... to be active.

humans food animals fish

more more less exercise moving

Activity means .... and doing

....

People who are .... active need

.... food to keep them going.

Q2 Dustin is going to run a big race tomorrow. He wants to eat foods that give him lots of energy. Draw (rings) round the **two** shopping lists that will give him the **best** food.

Shopping List
spaghetti
bread
bananas

Shopping List
cucumbers
apples
toothpaste

Shopping List
red wine
beefburgers
onion rings

Shopping List
pasta
potatoes
oatcakes

Mmm — I'm feeling hungry...

You need energy to do any sort of activity (even opening your eyes). To get energy you need to eat the right type of food. The more activity you do, the more food you need.

Balanced Meals

It is important to eat a balanced mixture of foods for energy and foods for growth.

Q1   Each plate has a mixture of foods. Write 'GROWTH' on all the foods that
help you grow. Write 'ENERGY' on all the foods that give you energy.

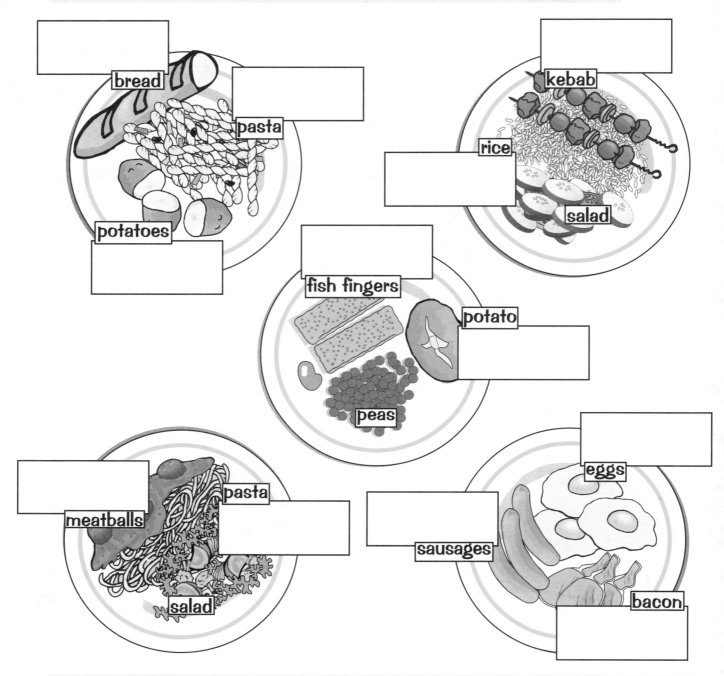

Q2   In a balanced meal you need growth foods, energy foods and vegetables.
Tick (✓) all the meals which you think are balanced. [CLUE: there are 3 balanced meals.]

A balanced meal — a bun on a tightrope...

There are millions of balanced meals you can eat. Every meal needs a bit of stodge
and a bit of growth food. And some vegetables — however much you hate them.

Eating a Balanced Diet

**People who don't eat all types of food
have to be extra careful about balancing their diet.**

Q1   Daisy doesn't eat meat or fish — she is a vegetarian.
Look at this shopping list and cross out any foods Daisy won't eat.

tomatoes	ham	tuna
broccoli	pasta	beef
onions	milk	cereal

Vegetarians have to make sure they get enough of the foods that help you grow.
Look at the pictures and write down three foods that will help Daisy grow.

....

Q2   Read the doctor's notes below, then fill in the missing word.

Charley is allergic to wheat — he can't eat

bread or pasta. He feels tired all the time.

I think it is because he isn't getting enough

[CLUE: It's either
'ENERGY' or 'GROWTH'.]

_ _ _ _ _ _ *from his diet.*

A balanced meal.

Tick (✓) the foods that Charley should eat to make himself feel better.

potatoes	tomato		chicken

☐	☐	☐	☐

Eat right — you'll be full of beans...

It doesn't really matter if you can't eat some foods. You just have to make up for it by
eating lots of other foods from the same group. Now what do I feel like for tea tonight...

Animal Diets

When scientists want to find out what animals eat,
they go and look at the animals in the wild.

Q1   Read these e-mails, then write what each of the animals eats.

From: Dr. Sam
To: Professor Rachel

Dear Rachel,
   What a day! At dawn the wolf pack killed a red deer down by the river. They ate most of it – but there was some left for the ravens.
   Later I stalked a wild boar. He was tearing shoots off a birch tree. When he'd eaten all the shoots he could reach he started digging up roots instead. Greedy pig!
Best wishes – Dr Sam.

Wolves eat ....

Ravens eat ....

Wild boar eat .... *and* ....

From: Professor Rachel
To: Dr. Sam

Dear Dr. Sam,
   Home at last – been out with the chimps. They were up a tree eating soft red fruits all morning. One of them found an ants' nest – she dipped a long, bendy stick in, then pulled it out and sucked off the ants.
   When the chimps moved to a nut tree about twenty grey parrots were there too. The chimps had to break the nuts open on rocks, but the parrots could crunch right through them!
Write soon, Rachel.

Parrots eat ....

Chimpanzees eat .... , ... *and* ....

Turkeys are so greedy — always gobbling...

You get the idea... to find out what animals eat you have to watch them, and see what they like. I don't much like the idea of eating ants — that proves I'm not a chimp!

Animal Diets

Different animals eat different foods. Monkeys eat different food from lions...
and you don't eat the same kind of food as your friend's hamster (I hope).

Q1   Write down what each of these pets eats. If you don't know the answer,
ask other people in your class, or look it up in a book.

[CLUE: Some of the animals may
eat more than one kind of food.]

Dogs eat:

....

....

Budgerigars eat:

....

....

Not all animals are fussy
about what they eat.

Goats eat:

....

....

Snakes eat:

....

....

Rabbits eat:

....

....

What's up, Doc? — AAARGH a talking rabbit...

A dog won't eat a lettuce and tomato salad, and you are not likely to see a budgerigar
tucking into a juicy steak. They like completely different kinds of food.

MINI-PROJECT

What Do Cats Eat?

Dr. Snooze has a new cat, and he wants to find out what to feed it.
He thinks that cats like fish, but he wants to do an investigation to make sure.

Q1 Which question should Dr. Snooze try to answer in his investigation?
Circle the good question from the ones below.

 When do cats go to sleep?

Why do cats need to eat?

 Do all cats eat fish?

What kind of music do cats like?

Q2 Dr. Snooze isn't sure which animals to use in his investigation. Tick (✔) the right box.

He should use cats and some dogs. ☐

He should only use cats. ☐

Q3 How many cats should he use in the investigation? Circle the right answer.

Every cat in the world.

Only one cat.

About 5 cats.

Q4 Dr. Snooze is thinking about how to write down the foods that cats eat.
Tick (✔) the box next to the good way to write them down.

Woof.
Miaow.
Woof.

Dr. Snooze had trouble speaking cat language.

Different types of fish should all be counted as just FISH. ☐

Different types of fish should all be listed one by one. ☐

Foods should be counted as TINNED or NOT TINNED. ☐

Any food that the cats eat should just be listed as FOOD. ☐

What's new pussycat — woah-oh-oh-oohoh...

Before you start doing an investigation, you need to decide what you want to find out.
If you write down all your ideas, you can cross out the bad ones straight away. Nice.

* Get your teacher to sing this really loud.

What Do Cats Eat?

Now you get to <u>do</u> the investigation to find out if all cats eat fish.
You need to keep a food diary for cats belonging to people in your class.

Q1 (Circle) the right words to finish off these sentences about how to do the investigation.

Dr. Snooze should [NOT / ONLY] look at cats.

The investigation will also be better if he studies lots of cats.

He should count all different types of fish as just

[FISH / FOOD] because he just wants to know if

all cats eat [CHOCOLATE / FISH] .

Q2 Read the instructions for doing a food diary, and then fill in the table below.
(If you can't do the investigation, use the spare results from the bottom of the page.)

Food diary instructions
1. Find five people in your class who have cats. Write their names in the top row of the table.
2. Ask the cat-owners what their cat ate the day before. Do this for three days in a row.
3. Each day, if the cat ate fish then put a tick (✔) underneath its owner's name.
4. If the cat did not eat fish then put a cross (✗) in the box.

If there are not many cat owners in the class, you could use other pets, as long as they are <u>all the same</u>.

Day 1					
Day 2					
Day 3					

SPARE RESULTS: Tim — ate fish on Day 1. Emily — ate fish on Day 1 and Day 3. Dave — didn't eat fish. Neil — ate fish on Day 2. Ian — didn't eat fish.

There is something fishy about this investigation...

Before you start an investigation you need to think. You need to work out <u>how</u> you are going to do the investigation. Then you can get on with the fun bit — actually <u>doing</u> it.

MINI-PROJECT

What Do Cats Eat?

That was the easy bit of the investigation. Now you have to show your results in a way that answers the question — "Do all cats eat fish?".

Q1   Fill in this tally chart, using your results from the food diary on page 11.

You just need to draw a line (like this I) for each cat in the right box. Then add the lines up in the 'Total' box.

	Tally — number of cats	Total
EATS FISH	....	....
DOESN'T EAT FISH	....	....

Q2   Complete this bar chart with the results from the tally chart.

If you are stuck, take a look at the bar charts section of the Maths Study Book.

Q3   Do you think the tally chart or the bar chart is better for showing the results? Why?

....

....

What do cats eat for breakfast...

Tables and bar charts are great. The way you show your results from investigations is important — it is no good doing investigations if you can't tell what the results mean.

KS2 Science Answers — Teeth and Eating

Q2: Depends on your data. This one is for the 'spare results'.

Q3: Depends on your results. Any sensible answer is OK.

Page 13 What Do Cats Eat?

Q1: Depends on your results.
For 'spare results', it's **"3** out of **5** cats ate fish."

Q2: Depends on your results.
For 'spare results', it's "**NO**".

Q3: The following should be ticked:
There were not enough cats in the investigation.
The investigation was too short to be sure of the results.

Q4: These words should be circled: **MORE, LONGER**.

Page 14 Your Teeth

Q1: Teeth are **white** and very **hard**.
They are used to **break** down food and they help us to **eat**.
These are the **gums**. They are soft and **pink**.
They help to **hold** the teeth in place.

Q2: Depends on which of your teeth have fallen out.

Page 15 Shapes of Teeth

Q1: These are my pictures. Yours can be a bit different — as long as they show the shapes of the teeth. It doesn't matter which type is drawn in which box.

2 in my bottom jaw.
2 in my top jaw.

4 in my bottom jaw.
4 in my top jaw.

4 in my bottom jaw.
4 in my top jaw.

NB The numbers above are if you have all your milk teeth.
You might have some teeth missing, or some extra adult teeth.

Page 16 Different Types of Teeth

Q1: These words should be ringed: **sharp, flat-edged**.

Q2: These words should be ticked: **gripping, tearing**.
The completed sentence is:
"Canines are long, pointy teeth. They are used for **gripping** and **tearing**."

Page 17 Different Types of Teeth

Q1: These words should be ringed: **BIG, BACK, BUMPY, GRINDING**.

Q2: Wolves: **canines** and **molars**.
Sheep: **incisors** and **molars**.

Page 18 Milk Teeth and Adult Teeth

Q1:
1) Root of milk tooth dissolves. → 2) Adult tooth grows.

4) Adult tooth is fully grown. ← 3) Milk tooth falls out.

Q2:

	Tooth decay	Being knocked out by accident	To make room for growing adult tooth
Child	✓	✓	✓

	Tooth decay	Being knocked out by accident	To make room for growing adult tooth
Adult	✓	✓	✗

Page 19 Milk Teeth and Adult Teeth

Q1:

Correct order for pictures in Simon's story:	1st Picture	2nd Picture	3rd Picture
	C	E	A

Correct order for pictures in Mick's story:	1st Picture	2nd Picture	3rd Picture
	B	F	D

Q2: These words should be ringed: **CHILD, DOES NOT, IMPORTANT**.

Page 20 Tooth Decay and Gum Disease

Q1: From top to bottom, the missing labels are:
"*Eating sugary food and drink leaves sugar in your mouth.*"
"*Bacteria eat the sugar and multiply.*"
"*The bacteria form a sticky slime called plaque.*"
"*Plaque rots the teeth and causes gum disease.*"

Page 21 Food and Teeth

Q1:

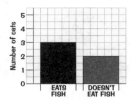

Q2: Missing words are: **sugary, mouth, bacteria, tooth decay, gum disease**.

Page 22 Preventing Tooth Decay

Q1: Any sensible poster is OK.

Page 23 Revision Questions

Q1: Any sensible answers are OK. Here are some you could put:
Fatty Food — butter, cheese; Fish — sardines, salmon;
Sugary Food — sugar, sweets; Meat — chicken, pork;
Starchy Food — bread, potatoes; Fruit and Veg — bananas, carrots.

Q2:

growth   growth   growth   activity

Q3: In order, filled-in words should be:
mixture, energy, vegetables, meat, beans.

Page 24 Revision Questions

Q1: Any sensible answers are OK, but these are 3 you could have:
Wolf — Deer
Chimpanzee — Ants
Wild Boar — Roots

Q2: Any sensible answers are OK, but these are 3 you could have:
Dog — Dry Dog Biscuits
Budgerigar — Sunflower Seeds
Goat — Hay

Q3: From left to right, should be: CANINE, INCISOR, MOLAR.

Q4: MOLARS
INCISORS
CANINES

Page 25 Revision Questions

Q1: Ticked sentences should be:
"Your first teeth are called milk teeth."
"When your milk teeth fall out, you get adult teeth."
"If an adult tooth rots and falls out, you won't grow another one."

Q2: When you eat sugary foods **some of the sugar is left in your mouth**.
You get more bacteria in your mouth **because they feed on the sugar**.
The bacteria in your mouth make **a sticky slime called plaque**.
Bacteria and plaque cause **tooth decay and gum disease**.

Q3: Because if you do, bacteria will grow all through the night.
(Any sensible version of that answer is OK.)

FOODS FOR ACTIVITY

Potatoes

Pasta

Rice

Bread

Sugar

FOODS FOR GROWTH

Fish

Lentils

Meat

Cheese

Beans

KS2 Science Answers — Teeth and Eating

Page 1 Background

Q1:

☐ ✓ ✓ ☐ ✓ ☐

Q2: a) Any sensible answer is OK.
     b) Any sensible answer is OK.

Q3: Any sensible answer is OK.

Page 2 Naming Foods

Q1:

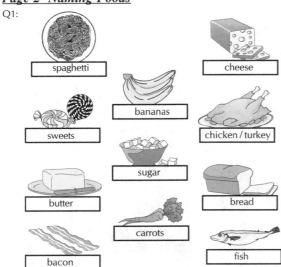

spaghetti	cheese
bananas	
sweets	chicken / turkey
sugar	
butter	bread
carrots	
bacon	fish

Page 3 Food Groups

Q1:

MEAT   FISH

FATTY FOOD   SUGARY FOOD

STARCHY FOOD   FRUIT AND VEGETABLES

Page 4 Foods for Growth

Q1: "So they can grow, move and stay healthy."
Q2: The left-hand plate should be ticked.
Q3: Beans, lentils, chicken (or turkey), fish, meat (or pork/lamb/beef).

Page 5 Foods for Activity

Q1: All *animals* including *humans* need *food* to be active.
     Activity means *moving* and doing *exercise*.
     People who are *more* active need *more* food to keep them going.

Q2:

Shopping List
spaghetti
bread
bananas

Shopping List
cucumbers
apples
toothpaste

Shopping List
red wine
beefburgers
onion rings

Shopping List
pasta
potatoes
oatcakes

Page 6 Balanced Meals

Q1&2:

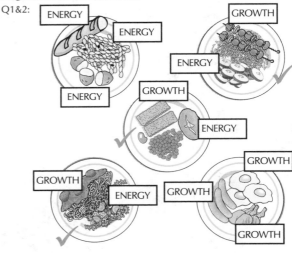

ENERGY ENERGY GROWTH ENERGY ENERGY GROWTH ENERGY GROWTH ENERGY GROWTH GROWTH GROWTH

Page 7 Eating a Balanced Diet

Q1: *Ham*, *tuna* and *beef* should be crossed out.
     "*Eggs*", "*cheese*" and "*beans*" should be written down.

Q2: Missing word is "*energy*".
     Potatoes and *rice* should be ticked.

Page 8 Animal Diets

Q1: Wolves eat *deer*. Ravens eat *deer*. Wild boar eat *shoots* and *roots*.

Q2: Parrots eat *nuts*. Chimpanzees eat *fruits*, *ants* and *nuts*.

Page 9 Animal Diets

Q1: Depends a bit on the research you do, but these are example answers:
     Dogs eat: meat, tinned food, dry dog biscuits.
     Budgerigars eat: seeds (e.g. grass, millet), bark, buds, cuttlefish bone.
     Goats eat: grass, hay, vegetables (e.g. cabbage, carrots).
     Snakes eat: meat (dried chicken, mice, insects).
     Rabbits eat: seeds, grass, lettuce, vegetables (e.g. cabbage, carrots).

Page 10 What Do Cats Eat?

Q1: "Do all cats eat fish?" should be circled.
Q2: "He should only use cats" should be ticked.
Q3: "About 5 cats" should be circled.
Q4: "Different types of fish should all be counted as just FISH" should be ticked.

Page 11 What Do Cats Eat?

Q1: Circled words should be: *ONLY*, *LOTS OF*, *FISH*, *FISH*.
Q2: Depends on your data. This one is for the 'spare results'.

	Tim	Emily	Dave	Neil	Ian
Day 1	✓	✓	✗	✗	✗
Day 2	✗	✗	✗	✓	✗
Day 3	✗	✓	✗	✗	✗

Page 12 What Do Cats Eat?

Q1: Depends on your data. This one is for the 'spare results'.

	Tally — number of cats	Total
EATS FISH	III	3
DOESN'T EAT FISH	II	2

What Do Cats Eat?

OK, you have your results — but you haven't finished yet.
Now you need to think about what the investigation tells you.

Q1 How many of the cats in your investigation ate fish? Write numbers in the spaces.

.... out of .... cats ate fish.

Q2 Do your results show that all 5 cats ate fish? Write YES or NO.

....

Q3 When Dr. Snooze did the investigation he found that all 5 cats ate fish, so he decided that all cats in the world eat fish. What problems might there be with the investigation? Tick (✓) the boxes next to the two possible problems.

There were too many cats in the investigation. ☐

Fish is poisonous to cats. ☐

There were not enough cats in the investigation. ☐

The investigation was too short to be sure of the results. ☐

Q4 What could make the investigation better if Dr. Snooze tried to do it again? Circle the correct words to finish off these sentences.

To make Dr. Snooze's investigation better, he could look at [FEWER / MORE] cats. Instead of writing down what they eat over three days, he could do a [LONGER / SHORTER] investigation.

Dr. Snooze tried to feed the wrong kind of cat.

...Mice Crispies...

Investigations can often be made better, and it is definitely worth thinking about whether your results make sense. That means the investigation will be even more fun next time...

Your Teeth

This page is about looking into your mouth
— I hope you have clean teeth and don't have a mouthful of cake...

Q1   Complete the sentences using the words from the bubble.

Teeth are ....
and very ....

They are used to ....
down food and they help
us to ....

bubble words: hold   break   white   pink   hard   eat   gums

These are the ....

They are soft and ....

They help to ....
the teeth in place.

Q2   Some of your teeth have probably fallen out. But they will be replaced by bigger,
better adult teeth. On the picture, colour in any of your teeth which have fallen out.

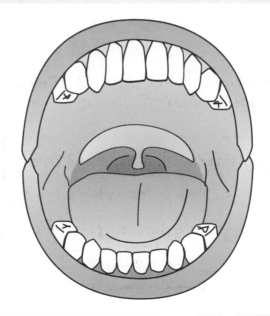

Tooth and gum — it's a sticky business...

When teeth start falling out it seems as if you are falling to pieces. But they are soon replaced
by bigger and better teeth — you might even get extra pocket money from the tooth fairy.

Shapes of Teeth

You have different types of teeth which are good for different things. Some are good for cutting, some for tearing and some for chewing — and all are good for grinning.

Q1   Look in your mouth — you will see **three** different shapes of teeth. Draw the three shapes (one in each box) and count how many of each are in your mouth.

Draw the tooth...

How many of this type of tooth do you have...

in your bottom jaw?

in your top jaw?

Draw the tooth...

How many of this type of tooth do you have...

in your bottom jaw?

in your top jaw?

Draw the tooth...

How many of this type of tooth do you have...

in your bottom jaw?

in your top jaw?

John found looking in his mouth tricky without a mirror.

Lots of tooth types — what a mouthful...

I reckon that's enough looking inside your mouth — the main things to remember are what the teeth and gums look like, and that teeth help us to eat by breaking up food.

Different Types of Teeth

Different teeth are used for different things. Incisors and canines are
at the front of the mouth. They are used for biting and cutting food.

Q1 This is one of my front teeth. It is called an **incisor**. I use it to
bite into my food. How does its **shape** make it good for biting?

Draw a (ring) round the words that
describe the **shape of an incisor**.

blunt

sharp

flat-edged

rounded

Incisor

Front   Side

Fred only had
one type of tooth...

Q2 **Canines** are at the front of your mouth but a bit to the side...
They are **long**, **pointy teeth**. What are they used for?

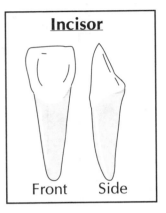

here...

Canine

Front   Side

Tick (✓) the **two best** uses.

grinding ☐   gripping ☐

tearing ☐   sucking ☐

Use the words you ticked to finish this sentence:

Canines are **long**, **pointy teeth**. They are used for

.... and

....

Fangs a lot...

The sabre-toothed tiger had huge canine teeth — also called "fangs". The long, sharp
teeth were great for hunting. The tiger could hold on to its prey to stop it getting away.

Different Types of Teeth

Molars are at the back of the mouth.
They are used for chewing food — ready for swallowing.

Q1   Molars are the big teeth at the back of your mouth.
Ring the correct words to explain what molars do.

Molars are [BIG / SMALL] teeth at the [FRONT / BACK] of the mouth.

They have a [BUMPY / SMOOTH] surface.

They are used for [BITING / GRINDING] food.

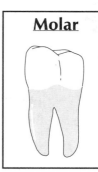

Molar

Different animals have different types of teeth.
A meat-eating animal has different teeth from a plant-eating animal.

Q2   I have a pet wolf and a pet sheep. They have different types of teeth.
Read these sentences then fill in the missing tooth names below.

Molars can crack and crush bones.
They are good for grinding up food.

Canines can stab and grip on to flesh.

Incisors are good for cutting through plants.

Wolves eat meat. Which 2 types of

teeth are important for this?

....

and ....

Sheep eat grass. Which 2 types

of teeth are important for this?

....

and ....

Just don't look TOO closely at a wolf's mouth...

The kind of teeth you need depends on what you eat.
Humans have **3** different types of teeth — but some animals have only **2** types.

Milk Teeth and Adult Teeth

Your first teeth are called your <u>milk teeth</u>.
Your milk teeth fall out one by one, and then you get <u>adult teeth</u>.

Q1   These pictures show how a milk tooth falls out and an adult tooth grows.
Choose the labels from the box, and write them out next to the correct picture.

I have done the first one for you.

Adult tooth is fully grown.
Milk tooth falls out.
Adult tooth grows.
Root of milk tooth fades away.

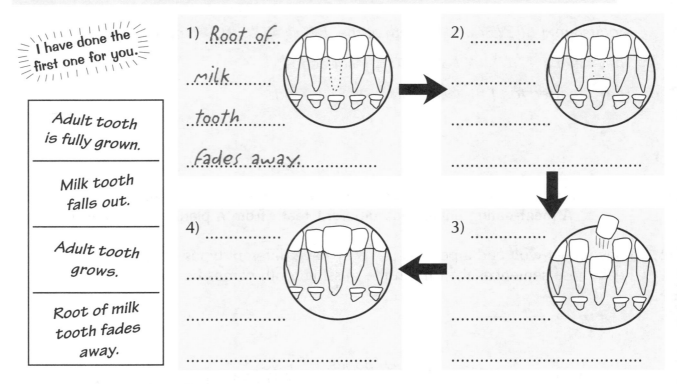

1) Root of milk tooth fades away.

2) ....

3) ....

4) ....

Q2   This table is about the ways that a **child** might lose a tooth. Fill in the three boxes.
Put a tick (✓) if a child could lose a tooth that way, and a cross (✗) if they couldn't.

I have done the first box for you.

	Tooth decay	Being knocked out by accident	To make room for growing adult tooth
Child	✓		

Now do the same thing again, but this time for an **adult**.

	Tooth decay	Being knocked out by accident	To make room for growing adult tooth
Adult			

If your teeth look like this, you should be worried.

My my Grandma, what big teeth you have...

You only have two sets of teeth — first milk teeth, then adult teeth. Simple as that.

Milk Teeth and Adult Teeth

Your milk teeth get replaced by adult teeth, but your adult teeth never get replaced — they have to last for the rest of your life.

Q1   Here are two mixed-up cartoons about Mick and Simon losing a tooth. **Simon** is **6** years old. **Mick** is **35** years old. Write letters in the spaces below to show what order the pictures should go in. I have done the first one for you.

Correct order for pictures in Simon's story:	1st Picture C	2nd Picture	3rd Picture ....

Correct order for pictures in Mick's story:	1st Picture	2nd Picture	3rd Picture ....

A A new tooth is showing in Simon's mouth.

B Mick has all his teeth.

C Simon's tooth is feeling wobbly.

D Mick's tooth will be missing forever.

E Simon's tooth has fallen out.

F A cricket ball has knocked out Mick's tooth.

Q2   Draw (rings) round the correct words in the brackets to finish off these sentences.

When a [CHILD / ADULT] loses a milk tooth, it gets replaced by an adult tooth.

If a grown-up loses a tooth, it [DOES / DOES NOT] get replaced

— that is why it is [IMPORTANT / NOT IMPORTANT] to look after adult teeth.

All the better to eat you with my dear...

Boxers wear plastic shields to protect their teeth from getting knocked out. Good idea.

Tooth Decay and Gum Disease

Look after your adult teeth — if you lose them you won't grow any more teeth.

Q1   The four pictures below show what happens if you don't look after your teeth.
Write in the words from the grey boxes next to the correct picture.

> Bacteria eat the sugar and multiply.

> The bacteria form a sticky slime called plaque.

> Plaque rots the teeth and causes gum disease.

> Eating sugary food and drink leaves sugar in your mouth.

Sugary drink

....
....
....

Bacteria

....
....
....

Plaque

....
....
....

Tooth decay   **Gum disease**

....
....
....

That is soooooooooooooo disgusting...

Yuk! — luckily the next two pages are all about how to stop tooth decay and gum disease.

Food and Teeth

Some types of food are worse for your teeth than others. (Here is a clue: SUGAR = ROT.)

Q1 Sugary foods are more likely to damage your teeth and gums.
Put a cross (✗) through **six** foods that are the most damaging to your teeth and gums.

Q2 Fill in the blanks in these sentences to say why some foods are bad for your teeth.
I have given you a few of the letters to help you out.

When you eat _s u g _ _ _ y_ foods like sweets and toffee,

lots of sugar is left behind in your _m o u _ _._.

This sugar is food for the _b a c t e _ _ __ that

cause plaque. Plaque causes _t _ _ t h   d e _ _ y_

and _g u _   d i s _ _ _ _._.

"He should pay
ME for taking
that thing".

Sugar — what a rotter...

Yep, sugar rots teeth all right. If you eat the right things you will get less plaque, but you have to do even more to keep your teeth healthy. That is what the next page is all about.

Preventing Tooth Decay

Going to the dentist, brushing your teeth and eating less sugar
all help to keep your teeth and gums healthy.

Q1   Draw a poster to show how to look after your teeth. Draw it in the big white box.
      Use the information below and use your own colours and pictures to make it look good.

Brush your teeth at least **twice** a day to remove plaque.

Don't eat **after** you brush your teeth in the evening. If you do, bacteria will grow all through the night.

Visit the **dentist**. They will remove plaque and check if your teeth are OK.

Don't eat lots of sugary foods.

LOOKING AFTER YOUR TEETH

Make way for the tooth train — chew, chew...

Don't forget — eat less sugary foods, brush, floss and visit the dentist. Simple.

Revision Questions

Revision means "going over things to help you learn them".
This page and the next two pages test everything you have learnt about teeth and eating.

Q1 Name two foods for each of these food groups.

FATTY FOOD
① ....
② ....

FISH
① ....
② ....

SUGARY FOOD
① ....
② ....

MEAT
① ....
② ....

STARCHY FOOD
① ....
② ....

FRUIT AND VEG
① ....
② ....

Q2 Are these foods good for **growth** or **activity**? Write **growth** or **activity** under each one.

Beans   Spaghetti

....

Q3 Fill in the blanks in these sentences about a balanced diet. Use the words from the tin.

Eating a balanced diet means you have to eat the

right .... of foods.

You have to eat the right amount of growth foods,

.... foods and ....

Vegetarians don't eat .... so they need

to eat growth foods like .... and lentils.

vegetables
energy   meat
mixture
beans

I saw Tintin do the cancan once...

If you can't remember something have a sneaky peek back through the book to help you.

Revision Questions

Look at all those lovely questions — get stuck in...

Q1 Name three wild animals and write one thing they eat.

Name of wild animal	What it eats

What do you call a woman with carrots in her ears?

Anything you like — she can't hear you.

Q2 Name three pet animals and write one thing they eat.

Name of pet	What it eats

Q3 Write the correct tooth name under each picture — INCISOR, CANINE or MOLAR.

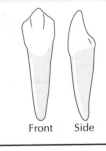

Front   Side

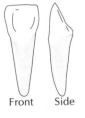

Front   Side

[_____]   [_____]   [_____]

Q4 Write in INCISORS, CANINES or MOLARS to finish off these sentences.

.... are good for grinding up food.

.... are good for cutting through plants.

.... can stab and grip on to meat. (CLUE: Vampires have big ones.)

Look at the size of those teeth...

Only one more page and you have finished. Don't forget to look after your teeth though.

Revision Questions

The last page of questions... sob, sob — don't worry though, there are a whole load more books bursting at the seams with questions for you.

Q1 Put a tick (✓) next to the sentences that are **true**.

☐ Your first teeth are called milk teeth.

☐ Milk teeth can't get tooth decay.

☐ When your milk teeth fall out, you get adult teeth.

☐ If an adult tooth falls out, you will grow another tooth.

☐ If an adult tooth rots and falls out, you won't grow another one.

Even astronauts in space have to brush their teeth.

Q2 Finish off all the sentences below by writing in the correct endings from the green box.

...tooth decay and gum disease.   ...a sticky slime called plaque.   ...some of the sugar is left in your mouth.   ...because they feed on the sugar.

When you eat sugary foods ....

You get more **bacteria** in your mouth ....

The **bacteria** in your mouth make ....

Bacteria and **plaque** cause ....

Q3 Why shouldn't you eat after you brush your teeth in the evening?

....

....

....

Twang, "I've got them last page blues"...

Go and eat some healthy food, clean your teeth and I will see you in the next book.

Index